a b c
RHYMES

by Carl Memling

**pictures by Rola... Rodriguez
and Grace...**

gb
GOLDEN PRESS
Western Publishing Company, Inc.
Racine, Wisconsin

Eleventh Printing, 1977

© Copyright 1970, 1964 by Western Publishing Company, Inc.
All rights reserved. Produced in U.S.A.

A

I'd like to be an acrobat,
an acrobat, an acrobat.
    I'd leap and vault
    And somersault
    And soar from this to that.
A is for Acrobat.

I'd like to have a clever bear,
a clever bear, a clever bear.
I'd teach him a trick
On a pogo stick
And watch him in the air.
B is for Bear.

I'd like to paddle a swift canoe,
a swift canoe, a swift canoe.
   I wouldn't fiddle-faddle;
   I'd paddle and I'd paddle
   Straight to Kalamazoo.
C is for Canoe.

I'd like to bang a big bass drum,
a big bass drum, a big bass drum.
   I'd go *babboom*
   From dawn to gloom
   Until my ears got numb.
D is for Drum.

E

I'd like to ride an elephant,
an elephant, an elephant.
I'd shout, "Hi ho!"
And off I'd go
And feel so elegant.
E is for Elephant.

F
     I'd like to go on a fishing boat,
a fishing boat, a fishing boat.
     I'd take a look
     And cast a hook
     And fish up what's afloat.
F is for Fishing Boat.

G I'd like to be a gondolier,
a gondolier, a gondolier.
I'd hum a song
As I glide along,
And everyone would cheer.
G is for Gondolier.

H

I'd like to ride
a prancing horse,
a prancing horse,
a prancing horse.
I'd hold on tight
With all my might
And keep him
on the course.
H is for Horse.

I'd like to live in a round igloo,
a round igloo, a round igloo.
I'd live on ice
And feel so nice
And never catch the flu.
I is for Igloo.

I'd like to saw with a jig saw,
a jig saw, a jig saw.
I'd sit right down
And saw a clown
And get a good guffaw.
J is for Jig Saw.

 I'd like to meet a kangaroo,
a kangaroo, a kangaroo.
   And I'd decide
   To take a ride;
   And there'd be a hullabaloo.
K is for Kangaroo.

L

I'd like to see a lioness,
a lioness, a lioness.
I'd hide in the shrubs
And watch her cubs;
And then go home, I guess.
L is for Lioness.

M

I'd like to climb
a mountain peak,
a mountain peak,
a mountain peak.
 And way up there
 I'd gasp for air;
 And rest up for a week.
M is for Mountain.

N

I'd like to watch a starry night,
a starry night, a starry night.
My eyes might ache,
But I'd stay awake
To watch the velvet sight.
N is for Night.

O

I'd like to sail the ocean deep,
the ocean deep, the ocean deep.
I'd steer by day
For Mandalay;
By night I think I'd sleep.
O is for Ocean.

P I'd like to play the piccolo,
the piccolo, the piccolo.
With care I'd touch
The keys and such,
And blow a tremolo.
P is for Piccolo.

I'd like to meet a lovely queen,
a lovely queen, a lovely queen.
I'd bare my brow
And then I'd bow
And share my nectarine.
Q is for Queen.

R I'd like to swing a tennis racket,
a tennis racket, a tennis racket.
   I'd take a ball
   Out on the mall
   And oh, how I would whack it!
R is for Racket.

S I'd like to hear a sea shell's song,
a sea shell's song, a sea shell's song.
 A song of the sea
 Would play for me;
 And I'd listen all day long.
S is for Sea Shell.

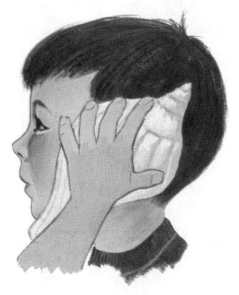

T I'd like to climb a cherry tree,
a cherry tree, a cherry tree.
 I'd call my pup
 And we'd go up
 For a Cherry Jamboree.
T is for Tree.

 I'd like to have a silk umbrella,
a silk umbrella, a silk umbrella.
I'd open it wide
And stand aside
To hold it over Stella.
U is for Umbrella.

V I'd like to play the violin,
the violin, the violin.
I'd scrape and squeak
A tune unique
And grin through all the din.
V is for Violin.

W

I'd like to grab a great big whale,
a great big whale, a great big whale.

His watery spray
Wouldn't wash me away;
I'd never let go of his tail.
W is for Whale.

I'd like to have a xylophone,
a xylophone, a xylophone.
I'd grab a hammer
And I'd klammer,
Till all the crows had flown.
X is for Xylophone.

X

I'd like to see a woolly yak,
a woolly yak, a woolly yak.
I'd stand and stare
At all his hair,
And the yak would
stare right back.
Y is for Yak.

Y

Z

I'd like to be a zookeeper,
a zookeeper, a zookeeper.
I'd lock all cages
And calm all rages
And even be the sweeper.
Z is for Zookeeper.